Stories About
S I K H
Traditions

Stories About
Sikh Traditions

Retold by

Dr. Kanwaljit Kaur
Inspectoress of Schools, U.K.
and
Chairperson, British Sikh Education Council, London

HEMKUNT

© Hemkunt Press

First Published 2006
Fifth Impression 2012

ISBN 81-7010-351-7

Published by

Hemkunt Press
401, Ansals Imperial Tower, C - Block Community Centre, Naraina Vihar,
New Delhi-110 028 (INDIA)
Tel.   :   2577-5349, 4141-2083
Fax   :   91-11-4540-4165
E-mail   :   hemkunt@ndf.vsnl.net.in
Website :   www.hemkuntpublishers.com

Printed at: Seven Seas Color (P) Ltd., New Delhi.

Contents

1

Guru Nanak feeding the Hungry

One day when Guru Nanak was just out of school, his father gave him twenty rupees and sent him to the market to buy some groceries to sell at their shop. 'Don't pay too much for the groceries, because when you get back, we can sell it for lots of money and make good profit,' said Nanak's father. Nanak was very excited at the prospect of starting a business, so he set off to the market. He decided to take his friend Bala with him as he was a bit older and had worked in a shop. He'd know what they should buy.

On the way to the market, they came across a group of holy men. They were very thin and their clothes were all tattered. Usually the people of the village would give them food but the harvest had been poor and there wasn't enough food to go around. They were very hungry and Nanak could not bear to see the men so hungry. He and Bala stayed for a while talking to them and then they went on their way to the market. Nanak bargained very hard, so that he would get as much food as he could. Bala was astounded at Nanak's capacity for bargaining. Nanak seemed too preoccupied to pay any attention to his friend. They bought lots of food items, fruits, vegetables, flour and lentils of all sorts.

After their shopping spree, instead of going home, Nanak went straight back to the holy men and started cooking the food for them. He hadn't been able to forget how hungry they were. 'You can't do that', shouted his friend Bala. 'What will your dad say when he finds out you've wasted his money? He'll never forgive you if you go home empty handed.' But Guru Nanak did not listen to his friend's advice. He could not leave the poor men to go hungry, even though he knew he'd upset his father. He thought it was important to share what he had. He said that helping and loving people that were hungry was also a way of showing love for God.

When the meal was over, Guru Nanak and Bala went back home. But Nanak was frightened to tell his father what he had done. So he sat under a tree outside while Bala went and told what had happened. Nanak's father was furious and shouted at Nanak for wasting money. 'I told you to spend the money wisely, to make a good bargain,' he said, 'I did', replied Guru Nanak, 'I fed the poor people, surely, there is no better bargain than feeding the poor'.

2

Guru Nanak Disappears

'He is gone, he is disappeared, he must have drowned', shouted Jamil, the servant of Sultanpur's chief. A small crowd gathered at the place where Jamil was shouting. When passers-by enquired the reason of Jamil's panic, he explained that, 'According to his daily routine, Nanak came to the river to bathe. I saw him go into the river and have a dip, but he did not come up. I have looked and looked for him, but he seems to have disappeared'. Other people came and looked. They saw his clothes lying on the bank, but no sign of him. Jamil decided to report Nanak's disappearance to the Chief of Sultanpur.

'Send all the divers to look for Nanak, he is my most trustworthy and honest officer. I am lost without him, who is going to keep accounts of my grocery store,' told the Chief to his servant, 'and you might as well ask the fishermen to cast their nets in the river in search of him. Find him, find him.'

But they could not find Nanak. Everybody thought that Nanak was drowned. His family and friends were in great mourning. Everyone in the town was sad, and they all missed him. 'I hope nothing has happened to Nanak', said Farida the street sweepress, 'many times, when I had no money, he gave me groceries and paid for them from his own pocket'.

A *fakir* (holy man) was lamenting Nanak's loss. He said, 'I remember when Nanak was given some money by his father to start a grocery shop. His father told him to become a successful businessman and spend the money wisely. Nanak went to buy the groceries and on the way, he met me and some Hindu *Sadhus*. We were hungry, we had not eaten any thing for a few days and we had no money to buy food. Nanak went to the market, bargained hard to get as much food as he could, and on his return he gave all the food to us. Later on we were told that Nanak's father was furious at not spending the money wisely, but Nanak had told him that there was no other better way of spending the money than feeding the hungry. Nanak's father was very disappointed in his son's actions and could not understand Nanak's love for God and God's people. He could not understand Nanak's higher thinking about God and thought that Nanak was a day dreamer, and did not want to be a wealthy man.'

Many people remembered Nanak's kindness and again and again visited the place where Nanak was last seen. Nanak was missing for three days. Then everybody thought that he was drowned, and gave up hope of finding even his body.

Nanak returned to his home. The family was overjoyed to see him alive and well. They asked him where he had been. But Nanak didn't say a word. More and more people came to visit him and asked him to explain his absence of three days. But Nanak did not say a single word during the first day, or the second day, and only on the third day he spoke. The first words he uttered were, 'There is neither a Hindu and nor a Muslim, but only man'. Everyone was puzzled at these words. They knew that there were Hindus and Muslims living in Sultanpur. They asked Nanak to explain the mystery behind these words.

Nanak replied that both Hindus and Muslims are God's people. God is not interested in the labels of Hindu or Muslim, but in the actions of people. How people behave themselves and treat other people. I had a vision of God, and now I must preach God's message. God is the Creator of all, and loves everyone. We all are God's children. We must not make distinctions between Hindu and Muslim on the basis of religion, but should live as brothers and sisters, as one family of God. The town people and his other holy companions realised that Nanak was a changed man. He was now giving them the message from God and they started calling him 'Guru', a teacher.

Guru Nanak left his job with the Chief of Sultanpur saying that, 'I am going to serve God and God alone'. He gave all his personal belongings to the poor and the needy and left with his friend Mardana to preach God's message. The Guru took four great missionary journeys: east as far as Assam, in India; south to Sri Lanka; north to Tibet, and west to Mecca in Saudi Arabia. During his travels of thousands of miles, the Guru preached about one God, treating all people as equals, respecting other peoples' faiths, and leading a good life.

3

Guru Nanak and the Leper

On one of his travels, Guru Nanak and his companion Mardana found themselves in a small town of Dipalpur. It was a dark stormy night, the Guru and Mardana drenched to the skin and ankle deep in mud, were scanning the countryside in the hope of finding a place to spend the night. But there was no sign of any building nearby where they could find shelter. There was nobody about in that stormy night to direct them to a nearby inn. So they had no alternative but to walk on. Guru Nanak and Mardana could not have been travelling in a worse situation than the one in which they found themselves. It was pitch dark with not a single star to give any light. The storm was raging. Travelling about in the country at the time of Guru Nanak was very difficult. The roads were in poor condition, muddy when wet and very dusty when dry. There were no road signs or maps to help the travellers.

As thunder crashed and lightning set the night sky ablaze, Mardana shouted with joy, 'I can see a little cottage right ahead of us. Surely they can't refuse us shelter on such a night like this. I am sure people who live there will give us some place to sleep for the night'. The hope of finding a dry place to spend the night rose their spirits and they walked quickly and hopefully towards the cottage. Soon they reached the place, it was a dilapidated little hovel of a cottage. Mardana knocked at the door. But there was no reply.

The hut belonged to a leper. He was not used to any visitors, as his terrible disease made him an untouchable, an outcaste from society. He suffered from constant pain from the wounds and spent most of his time feeling sorry for himself. He made no effort to busy himself with the house work of cleaning and tiding the place, but sat there surrounded by a suffocating smell brooding over his misfortune of having to put up with the disease.

When Mardana knocked again, a shrill angry voice replied from inside the hut, 'Go Away, leave me alone. I am a leper, if you come any nearer, you will catch the disease.' Mardana knocked again and Guru Nanak said, 'Do not worry, we know you have the disease, we have come to help you'. At this, the inhabitant of the little hovel opened the door. Mardana and the Guru could see that the man's whole body was diseased, his room was filthy and rather smelly. The leper shouted, 'Help me! Why should you help me? Everyone, including God has turned His back on me. My family and friends have rejected me, the villagers run away from me. I am in constant pain. There is no cure for my disease. No one can help me. If you are not careful you might end up catching the disease'.

The Guru ignored what the leper was saying and asked if he and his companion could share his place for the night. Without waiting for an answer the Guru

entered the cottage and started to clean the mess. This horrified the leper. He never had any human friends. Being rejected by relatives, mocked and teased by the village children and shunned by society, he had given up hope and self-esteem and had nothing but self-pity.

The Guru listened patiently to the leper's complaints, and then told him to face up to life and not sit moaning and grumbling about his fate. What the leper needed was hope and have self-esteem restored. The discourse with the Guru cured the leper's mind, for the leper saw that it was wrong to waste his life in bitterness. Once the mind was cured, the Guru set about helping to cure the leper's body. He bathed the leper, wrapped his wounds in clean sheets and blessed him. In the morning, the legend has it that when the leper unwrapped himself, he found his body was completely cured. The bitterness against the human race too was gone and once more he turned to God, not to curse Him but to praise Him. Now he could think about joining his family and friends and doing some useful work to help others rather than wasting his days in self-pity.

4

Two Villages

'I am hungry and am exhausted. I can't walk another step. And there is no sign of any village, where we can stop and have food and bed for the night,' complained Mardana. Guru Nanak and Mardana had been travelling for days preaching God's message. They had been sleeping rough in the jungles and had survived on whatever wild fruits they could find.

To their immense joy and relief, Mardana saw some smoke rising in the distance. They rushed towards it and as they turned the corner, they could see the walls of a village. Their spirits rose at the thought of getting food and lodgings and an opportunity to rest and regain their strength. Mardana went to the village, while the Guru sat waiting outside.

On entering the village, Mardana politely requested for food. But the villagers did not welcome Mardana. Some of them even made fun of him and others threw stones at him. On meeting such hostility, Mardana had no alternative but to leave empty handed.

On arriving back at the place where the Guru was sitting, Mardana complained, 'I have never met such inhospitable, rude, selfish and violent people all my life. We better move and find some other place before the night falls'. According to the Guru's usual custom, he got up and said a little prayer, 'I hope these villagers will always have a home here and they remain happy and contented in this village'. Mardana did not understand why the Guru was blessing such inhospitable people, but he said nothing and walked on.

Soon they found another village. Mardana again went into the village and timidly asked a villager for a place where he and his companion could get some food and spend the night. Mardana had hardly finished his request, when the villagers offered food and lodgings for him and his companion. It was not long before the Guru and Mardana were tucked in bed, sleeping away their exhaustion.

After staying for a few days, the Guru thanked the villagers for their hospitality and left. Again, just outside the village, the Guru stopped and prayed that the villagers of this village would scatter far and wide. Mardana was astonished to hear this prayer. He asked the Guru, the reason for blessing the inhospitable people of first village to continue to live there happily, and praying that

the very hospitable people of the second village to lose their homes and hearths and move on to new places. At this, the Guru replied that, 'Where ever the hospitable villagers will go they will take their goodness with them and will teach their kindness to others. That is why I want them to move. It will be better for the human race, if the selfish people of the first village remain settled so that they do not infect others with their meanness'.

5

Lalo and Bhago

These days we often hear about greed and sleaze amongst politicians and those in business. Stories of pensioners being mugged and robbed off a few pounds by our young people. At a time when everyone wants to seem to get rich quickly whatever the cost, it is useful to remember the story of Lalo and Bhago.

On one of his travels, Guru Nanak reached Eminabad and accepted Lalo's invitation to stay with him. Lalo was a humble carpenter. There was a lot of gossip about the Guru staying with a poor low caste carpenter, but the Guru ignored the gossip.

One day, a very wealthy man Bhago, decided to give a feast and invited all the rich and famous people including many holy men. Guru Nanak was also invited. It was considered a great honour to be asked to dine with a rich man like Bhago. 'No, I am not accepting Bhago's invitation to his feast,' Guru Nanak told Lalo. 'Your food is good enough for me, I don't need the dainty food of rich people'.

When Bhago heard that the Guru has refused his invitation he was furious. He came to the Guru and asked, 'Why have you declined to attend my sumptuous feast in favour of coarse food of a poor carpenter. You insult me by refusing to come to my feast'.

The Guru replied, 'Lalo's simple bread is earned by honest labour. It is pure and good to eat. It tastes like pure milk to me. But you have grown rich by exploiting and taking advantage of the poor. You live on the poor like a blood sucking insect. Your food is stained with the blood of the poor'.

'Nonsense!,' shouted Bhago in an angry voice. The Guru smiled, and then as the legend says, in one hand he took a piece of bread from Lalo's house, and in the other a piece of bread from Bhago's house, and he squeezed them both. Milk dripped from Lalo's bread and blood from Bhago's bread! The rich man realised his mistake and promised the Guru to devoting his life in helping the poor and needy.

The Guru says;

'He alone has found the right way
Who eats what he earns through toil
And shares his earnings with others'.

Bowl of Milk

In today's world, people of different religions still argue over religious differences, each claiming that they alone are right. Religions need to do more than just claiming superiority over each other that they are the only ones with all the moral goodness. Religious people should demonstrate goodness by practising the teachings of their religious teachers and thus spread goodness in the world, and contribute to the spiritual, moral, social and cultural development of our young people, our future generations.

Guru Nanak had been travelling for many days and nights with his Muslim companion Mardana. They had little to eat and not a place to sleep for the night except the open fields. Eventually they arrived at the city of Multan, which was well known for its generosity to holy men. The priests there were rich and holy men lived in comfort as people came to them for their advice and in return gave them presents of money.

When the priests heard that Guru Nanak and Mardana had arrived, they were worried. They didn't want to share their good fortune with anyone else. They sent a messenger to the Guru with a bowl full of milk, to indicate that the city was already full of holy people and there was no room for anyone else. The messenger carefully carried the bowl to the Guru, making sure none spilt, and handed the bowl to the Guru. But instead of taking it, the Guru bent down and plucked a beautiful jasmine flower which was growing nearby. He dropped the flower in the bowl of milk and gave the message, 'Just as there is room for the jasmine flower to scent the bowl full of milk, so there is always room for holiness and goodness in this world'.

The Qazi and the Nawab

*T*hese days we are always on the search for quick fix solutions. We even use prayer in this way. We often assume that by saying prayer we immediately reach our ultimate goal. The Sikh Gurus said, 'Truth is high but higher still is truthful living'. Praying is not just saying the prayers but we should understand and act upon the advice contained in the prayers. A story from Sikh scriptures reminds me of this.

Once Guru Nanak was approached by a Nawab who was a head of a small principality, and a Qazi, a priest. They said to the Guru that, 'You say that Hindus and Muslims are all children of the one and the same God. We all pray to the same and only one God. If that is true, then why not come and pray in the mosque with us.' To this, the Guru readily agreed.

When the Qazi stood up to pray, everyone stood up and joined him except the Guru who remained

seated. At the conclusion of the prayer the Nawab asked why the Guru didn't join them. The Guru said that he wanted to join in the prayer as he had promised, but felt that both the Qazi and the Nawab weren't present at the prayer. At this, both the Qazi and the Nawab argued that they were there and had been praying.

'But where were your minds?' asked the Guru. He then astonished the Nawab by suggesting quite accurately that the Nawab was busy thinking of buying horses in a market in Kabul, a place that was well known for quality horses. Then the Qazi asked, 'But what about joining me. I was praying'. The Guru replied that he was busy thinking of his newly born foal who was not tied securely and was afraid just in case it fell in the well. They both realised that just saying the prayer without reflecting is not enough. It should be reflected upon, understood and practised in our daily lives.

8

Time for Rejoicing

'Congratulations, you have given birth to a beautiful, healthy boy', said the midwife and handed the newly born baby to his mother. Mata Gujri was delighted to hold her first born child in her arms. She looked and admired the perfectly formed tiny hands and arms, legs and feet and then looked at his handsome face. It seemed that the mother was lost in deep thoughts, 'What are you thinking?' These words of the midwife broke Mata Gujri's trance. 'Thinking, what am I thinking? I can't think, I am too happy to think. I have waited, it seems almost an eternity to have this baby,' she replied.

The birth of a baby is always a time for rejoicing. The family, the friends, the relatives, the neighbours, everyone eagerly awaits the arrival of a new baby. But the birth of this baby was even more special. Mata Gujri and her husband Guru Tegh Bahadur, the ninth Guru of the Sikhs, were both in their forties and had waited a long time to have a child of their own. Guru Tegh Bahadur was away from Patna in Bihar at the time of the baby's birth. Mata Gujri amidst great festivities and rejoicing named the baby Gobind Rai. Friends and relatives brought presents for the child and Mata Gujri gave *laddus* (sweets) to every one who came to congratulate.

Far away from Patna, in the city of Karnal in Punjab, a holy Muslim *Pir* Bhikhan Shah did something very unusual on the day Gobind Rai was born. According to his daily routine, he faced Mecca towards the west and said his prayers. But as soon as he concluded his prayers, he turned towards Patna to the east and made a deep bow. His disciples were surprised to see their *Pir* bowing to the east. They asked him to explain the reason. The *Pir* replied, 'A holy child has taken birth in the east. I am paying my respects to him'.

Soon afterwards *Pir* Bhikhan Shah along with his disciples and servants set out for Patna to see the holy child. The journey was long and hard. They had to cover a distance of hundreds of miles. *Pir* was anxious to travel fast. He had an important mission to achieve. After travelling for many weeks, the party arrived at Patna. The *Pir* left the party of his disciples and went alone to a sweet shop owned by a Hindu. He bought an earthen pot full of *laddus* (a sweet which in India is traditionally given to friends and relatives on happy occasions). Then he went to another shop owned by a Muslim. He bought a second earthen pot full of *laddus*. After this shopping, he rejoined his disciples and went to Mata Gujri's house. There he requested to see the new born child.

Mata Gujri was informed that a holy man and his disciples wished to see Gobind Rai. She was also told that the holy man was adamant that he would leave the place only after he has seen the child. Mata Gujri was naturally reluctant to show the child to the strangers. But on seeing the devotion on the *Pir*'s face, she invited them into her house.

As soon as Pir Bhikhan Shah saw Gobind Rai, he respectfully bowed to him. Then he placed the two earthen pots full of *laddus* in front of Gobind Rai and sat down with his gaze fixed on the holy child. Gobind Rai without any hesitation, covered one pot with his left hand and the other pot with his right hand and gave the *Pir* a beaming smile. The *Pir* was thrilled with Gobind Rai's reaction to his pots. He made a deep bow and got up to leave.

Pir's confused disciples said, 'We are unable to understand what we have seen. Please explain it to us'. The *Pir* replied, 'I wanted to know whether this holy child would be the friend of Hindus or Muslims. I had thought that if he was to be the friend of Hindus, he would put his hand on the pot bought from the Hindu's

shop and if he was to be the friend of the Muslims he would put his hand on the pot I got from a Muslim's shop. The child has understood my thoughts and has answered my questions. He has covered both the pots, showing that both Hindus and Muslims will be equally dear to him. He will not make any distinction on religious grounds. The holy child's action has given me immense pleasure'.

The *Pir* and his party then bade farewell to the child and his mother and began their journey back to Punjab. The holy child, Gobind Rai became the tenth Guru of the Sikhs after the martyrdom of his father Guru Tegh Bahadur. He became known as Guru Gobind Singh. Pir Bhikhan Shah remained a devoted admirer and a friend of the Guru throughout his life.

9

Bhai Kanahiya

'Water, water', cried a soldier. Fighting had been very fierce for several days and from early morning both sides had been giving each other a very tough time. The hot sun burnt down relentlessly on the dusty plain. Sweat poured off the soldiers' brows and their bodies flagged with exhaustion. By evening the battlefield was strewn with the dead and the dying. The dead and the wounded lay side by side, even heaped together on the ground. The air was filled with cries of pain from the wounded.

Guru Gobind Singh, the tenth and the last human Guru and the Sikh community were defending themselves with very meagre resources against the Emperor's mighty armies. The Guru had preached equality of all people irrespective of their background, caste, colour or creed. He taught that, 'There is but one race and that is of human beings.' The bigoted Mughal Emperor Aurangzeb could not accept equality of all human beings. He wanted to convert his subjects to Islam and he committed untold atrocities on his non-Muslim subjects. Guru Gobind Singh and the whole Sikh community were subjected to incredible suffering. They were thrown out of their homes and had to take up arms to defend the innocent public.

On this occasion, when the Emperor's forces attacked Guru Gobind Singh, Kanahiya was assigned the duty of providing water to the wounded. As dusk fell, Kanahiya slung a thick water bag around his neck and walked on the battlefield, picking his way through the wounded and dying soldiers. He would bend down and give water to the wounded and thirsty soldiers. He heard the cry 'Water, water', and quickly moved towards the sound and gave water to the dying soldier. At every sign of life, Kanahiya poured a few drops of precious water into the mouths of the wounded. Many of them revived and his cheerful, loving words brought them hope.

A group of weary Sikh soldiers spotted him and recognised the water carrier. As they watched him more closely, they noticed that he was giving water not only to the Sikh soldiers but also to the wounded enemy soldiers as well. One Sikh soldier shouted, 'Hey Kanahiya, what are you up to? Can't you tell the difference between the Sikh and the enemy soldiers? Have you taken leave of your sense? We fight all day for our lives

and you are giving water to revive our enemies?' But Kanahiya did not pay any attention to the Sikh soldier and carried on giving water to all friends and foes alike.

One Sikh soldier grabbed Kanahiya and said, 'If you don't stop helping the enemies, I'll... ' At this, one of the other Sikh soldiers put a hand on his shoulder and stopped him. He suggested, 'I think we should take him to Guru Gobind Singh and not take the law in our hands. He would know what to do with Kanahiya'. They all agreed and hurried to find the Guru.

On reaching the Guru's tent they complained bitterly, 'Are we supposed to be fighting the enemy or not? How can we ever win? Kanahiya is giving water to the enemy soldiers and reviving them to fight against us. He is either a traitor or he has gone mad'.

The Guru listened to them calmly and asked his Sikhs to bring Kanahiya. The Guru was not going to jump to any conclusion. He was not called a 'true Guru' for nothing. The Sikh soldiers brought Kanahiya as a prisoner. The Guru said, 'My Sikhs have complained that you have been helping the enemy soldiers and you are a traitor to the Sikh cause. What have you got to say to this charge? Please explain.' 'It is not true', replied Kanahiya. 'I am a water carrier,' he said. 'It's my duty to take the water to the wounded and the dying. So when the battle ended today, as usual, I took the water round to the injured soldiers.' 'This is true, but I saw him with my own eyes giving water to the enemy', interrupted a Sikh.

The Guru again asked if this charge of giving water to the enemy was true. Kanahiya said, 'When I was taking water round the battlefield, I saw no Muslims and no Sikhs, no friends no enemies, I saw only God's people. I was practising what you taught us.' 'Oh, Kanahiya, you are a true Sikh,' said Guru Gobind Singh, hugging him tightly, eyes filled with joyful tears he reminded everyone that, 'We are fighting this war to hold on to our faith. Our faith teaches us that everyone is equal before God's eyes with a right to life and freedom to find God in their own way. Kanahiya has shown us the true spirit of service to God's creation. You are a true brother to everyone. From now onwards you will be called *'Bhai'* (meaning brother). He also ordered that *Bhai* Kanahiya should also be given an ointment so that he could also apply it on the wounds of injured soldiers— both Sikh and Muslim alike.

So the best way to celebrate the Guru's birthday is to act like Bhai Kanahiya and follow the Guru's teachings:

'Grant me this boon, O God, from Your greatness
May I never refrain from righteous acts
May I fight without fear all foes in life's battle
With confident courage'.

10

Story of Vaisakhi

It was on the Vaisakhi day in 1699 that Guru Gobind Singh, the tenth Sikh Guru tested his community to see whether his Sikhs were brave enough to stand up for their beliefs, even in difficult times.

The Guru, stood in front of more than 50,000 Sikhs, holding a sword in his hand. He said, 'I need a Sikh, who is willing to sacrifice his life for God and the Guru'. There was a stunned silence. Many people thought that they misheard the Guru and many others thought, perhaps the Guru was joking. But they could see a sword shining in the Guru's hand. The Guru repeated again, 'Is there anyone who is willing to give up his life for the Guru and God.' The Guru repeated his call for the third time and waited patiently. This time Daya Ram got up, with folded hands, he said to the Guru, 'I claim to be your humble Sikh, and for you, my Guru I willingly give my life.' The Guru took him by his hand and led him to a tent.

The crowd waited eagerly to see what the Guru would do next. To their dismay, they saw the Guru come out of the tent with his sword apparently dripping with blood and asked for another volunteer. The stunned crowd looked in disbelief at each other. Some of them were too shocked to say anything, while some others quietly slipped away from the assembly. Some Sikhs went to complain to the Guru's mother and others complained to his wife about the Guru's behaviour. On the Guru's third call, another brave Sikh came forward to offer his life. Again the Guru took him into the tent, and reappeared with the sword in his hand and asked, 'I want another true Sikh. Who else is willing to die for the Guru and God.' By this time people assumed that the Guru was serious and meant to take his Sikhs' lives. Many muttered angry words, and others in fear of losing their lives, left.

Another brave Sikh came forward to give his life. Again the Guru took him to the tent. This happened three times more. Altogether the Guru asked for the lives of five Sikhs. After the fifth time, the Guru took a little longer coming out of the tent. The crowd gasped in disbelief when they saw that the Guru was followed by the five Sikhs he had taken into the tent. The Sikhs and the Guru had their hair tied neatly under their turbans and were dressed in resplendent clothes. The Guru explained that he had no intention of harming

anyone. He wanted to test the courage of Sikhs and willingness to die for their faith. These five Sikhs had passed the test. The Guru explained, 'These five Sikhs have shown courage, they are my *panj piare* (five beloved ones)'.

The Guru then asked for an iron bowl, *khanda* (a two edged sword) and water to be brought. The Guru poured water into the iron bowl and began stirring it with the *Khanda* while reciting the five prayers. The Guru's wife added some *patasas* (sugar). The Guru accepted his wife's contribution saying, 'You have made the ceremony complete, a resolve of steel should be combined with a sweetness of temperament'. The Guru gave *amrit* to the *panj piare*, the first five members of the community, then he knelt before them, and in a remarkable gesture of humility, asked them to initiate him into the new community of equals in which master and disciple were one.

Then the Guru gave Sikhs a uniform, distinguishing symbols of Sikh beliefs which would serve as a badge of Sikh identity. No longer could Sikhs hide in the anonymity of the crowd even in difficult times. These symbols are called 5 K's, as they begin with the Punjabi letter 'K'. These are: *kesh* (uncut hair) sign of saintliness and visible identity to the Sikhs; *kanga* (wooden comb) to keep the hair tidy and well groomed; *kara* (steel circular bracelet) to remind Sikhs their link with God;

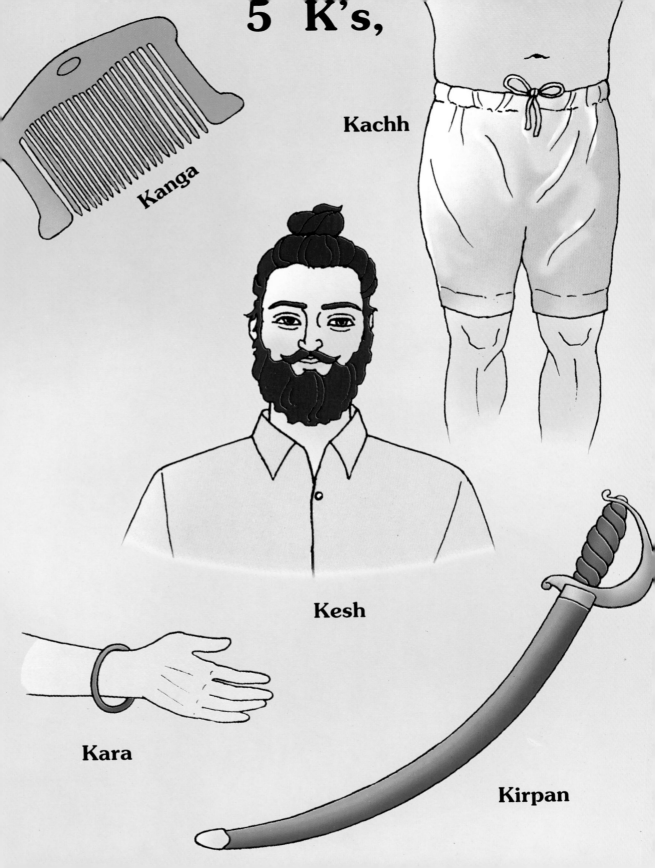

5 K's,

Kanga

Kachh

Kesh

Kara

Kirpan

kachh (shorts) an active dress instead of loose unstiched *dhoti* so as to be always ready to fight anywhere against injustice and *kirpan* (sword) is for self protection and to be used as a last resort to resist oppression and to defend the weak. The most distinctive of these five articles is uncut hair. Sikh men do not shave their beards or the hair of their head. They wear turbans on their neatly tied hair. Women keep their uncut long hair loose or braided or tied in a bun.

In a move to end social divisions in the new community of equals, the Guru asked all male Sikhs to drop their surnames, then linked to caste or occupation, indicating superiority or inferiority of status in society, and take the common name 'Singh', literally 'lion', a reminder of the need for courage. At the same time, the Guru gave Sikh women the name or title 'Kaur', literally 'princess' to emphasise dignity and complete equality.

On that historic Vaisakhi day, the *amrit* was offered to whoever was willing to abide by the Guru's rules. By the end of the day, 20,000 men and women had taken *amrit* and decided to follow the Guru who also took the name Singh and was now known as Guru Gobind Singh.

11

Maharaja Ranjit Singh

Maharaja Ranjit Singh was a ruler of Punjab in India of the early 19th century. Though he was a Sikh, but unlike the rulers of his time, he dictated that his government was a secular and not only a Sikh Government. His subjects included Hindus, Muslims and Sikhs. He made sure that each and every one of his subjects was treated with justice, irrespective of their religion. The Maharaja not only allowed freedom of conscience and worship but donated gifts and estates to other religions including Hindu and Muslim places of worship.

Once, some Muslim residents of a village complained to the Maharaja that Sikh and Hindu residents of the village are objecting to the *Imam's* (priest) traditional 'call to prayer'. It involved the priest calling in a loud, shrill voice from the top of a mosque five times a day, telling Muslims that it was time for prayers. The Maharaja called the Sikhs and Hindus who objected to the 'call to prayer' by the *Imam*. On enquiring, the Maharaja was told that a call to prayer five times a day interrupted their work. Then the Sikhs also said that 'we have not forgotten how we were persecuted when the Muslims ruled over us. We were not allowed to practise our religion and were to be killed on sight and rewards of money were given to those who brought a head of a Sikh's body. Now, during our Sikh rule, the Muslims should forget their religious customs and obey us'.

The Maharaja thought for a while and then said, 'Our Sikh Gurus taught us that everyone has the right to worship the manner of his or her choice and the ninth Guru, Guru Tegh Bahadur gave his life defending the right of Hindus. So we must not copy the intolerance of others but do what is right. Sikh religion teaches respect for all religions. The Moghul rulers were wrong in not allowing Hindus and Sikhs to practise their religion. Two wrongs can never make a right. However, we must find a solution, on the issue of loud shrill voice of an *Imam* calling Muslims to prayer disturbing you and interfering with your work'.

The Maharaja asked the Hindus and Sikhs to go away for a week and find a solution acceptable to both Muslims and Hindus and Sikhs. Despite many meetings and discussions, they could not reach a decision. After a week, they came to the Maharaja and expressed their inability to find a solution. At this, the Maharaja asked

the Sikhs and Hindus that, 'You take the responsibility of going around the village five times a day at the right time informing all Muslims living in the village that it was time for prayers. After all, the *Imam* does exactly that. If you agree to this, then I can tell these people to ask the *Imam* not to stand on the minaret and use his shrill voice, as it disturbs others.'

The Hindus and Sikhs looked at each other and replied, 'This is an impossible task. How can we run around five times a day, to the shops, houses and fields of these people exactly at the same time informing them that it is the time for prayers? It will need many people running around to do so. We have our jobs to do.' At this, the Maharaja replied, 'Then let the *Imam* carry on with the call. We must be tolerant of others and not interfere with the religious practices of others. We should follow our Gurus' teachings and make sure that people of all religions can worship in the manner of their choice.'

12

The Day we had Langar

'Hurry mum, its after one and I have to be at Simran's by two. I don't want to be late,' said Peter as he pulled on his coat. Peter was excited. He was going to help his friend Simran Singh cook dinner for three hundred people at the Sikh temple.

When Peter reached Simran's house, he said good bye to his mum and ran into the hall. It was full of groceries which Simran's dad was loading in the car. 'Can Peter and I help?' asked Simran. 'Of course you can, but don't try to lift heavy packets. I'll do those,' said dad as he bent down to lift some tins, 'Why don't you help put the kitchen rolls and napkins inside the car while I load the boot'.

'Where are you taking all these huge tins, packets and sacks of rice and flour' asked Peter. 'To the gurdwara of course', replied Simran. 'What's a gurdwara?' asked Peter. 'It's a place where Sikhs meet and pray to God', answered Simran. 'In the same building we also have a hall where we all eat together after the service, and a large kitchen where we prepare the food. If you didn't have to go home by six o'clock you could sit and eat with everyone as well', said Simran. 'But I am not a Sikh, I am a Christian,' Peter replied. 'That does not matter,' replied Simran. 'Everyone who comes to the gurdwara can join in cooking, serving and eating.' Peter was a bit confused. 'Do you do this every week', he asked. 'Yes, and different families take it in turn', explained Simran. 'We're doing it this week because mum thought it was a good way to celebrate my birthday'.

The car stopped near a large building with a bright orange flag outside. 'This is our gurdwara', said Simran. The two boys took off their shoes before going upstairs to visit the prayer hall. Simran pointed to a large stage with a beautiful canopy. 'That's where we keep our holy book, the *Guru Granth Sahib*', he said excitedly. As they walked along a beautiful blue carpet towards the stage, they saw that the holy book was covered with purple cloth with gold embroidery. 'It's beautiful,' whispered Peter. Simran bowed before the holy book and they each placed a ten pence coin in a large steel box nearby.

'The money goes to charity', explained Simran.

Simran and Peter then came downstairs and went straight to the kitchen. They saw men and women busy, chopping onions, opening tins of tomatoes, cutting cauliflower and peeling potatoes. He saw lots of things

being cooked in huge saucepans and said to Simran's mum, 'Aren't the saucepans huge. They are bigger than my baby's bath tub.' 'Yes, we do need big saucepans for cooking food for over 300 people', said Simran's mum. She was cooking lentils and she let Peter stir the pot with a huge ladle. On the next stove, Simran's dad was busy putting small pieces of cauliflower and potatoes in another large saucepan, which had fried onions, tomatoes and spices. Next to him, Simran's aunt Reema was cutting tomatoes and cucumbers. Grand dad was busy washing rice and nearby, onions were sizzling in a large saucepan.

'What sort of meat are you cooking,' asked Peter. 'We don't have meat,' replied Simran 'The food in the gurdwara is always vegetarian so that people who do not eat meat can also join in.' 'What's for dessert?' asked Peter. 'Come and I'll show,' said Simran as he pulled Peter towards a table with lots of boxes of delicious looking sweetmeats.

'Boys, wash your hands' then I'll show you how to make chapatis', called Simran's mum. Peter and Simran washed their hands and were shown how to make small balls of dough. They were quite good in making small balls. Simran's mum and aunt rolled these balls into circular flat shapes and two other women cooked them on a large hot plate. Peter and Simran tried to roll some balls to make circular shapes for chapatis. Peter rolled one and it got stuck to the rolling pin, and Simran couldn't stop laughing. 'I can make better chapatis,' he boasted. He tried rolling a ball of dough but it also stuck to the rolling pin. Now it was Peter's turn to laugh. Simran's mother said, 'Put some dry flour on the rolling pin and some on the board, this way the dough won't stick'. The boys tried again and soon they were having a lovely time making lots of different shapes out of the dough.

At six o'clock, Simran's dad reminded Peter that it was time to go home. The two boys reluctantly left the kitchen and went with Simran's dad to Peter's house.

Peter could not wait to tell his family what he had been doing. He shouted, 'We have been cooking lots and lots of food for three hundred people.' 'Lucky then,' said Peter's mum, 'we've had a power failure and I haven't been able to cook anything,' she said.

Simran's dad had an idea. 'Why don't you join us in the gurdwara,' he asked. 'Please, please mum, can we? I want to taste all the food that I saw being cooked,' asked Peter. Peter's parents said they would love to, and they all reached the gurdwara at eight p.m. After visiting the prayer hall, they joined everyone in the common meal.

Peter's family loved the food and got to know lots of new people. They felt like they were part of a new family. 'Thank you so much for sharing your food with us', they said as they left for home. 'Peter, did you enjoy your day with Simran?' asked Peter's dad. 'Yes, I had a very exciting day,' replied Peter. 'What did you like best,' asked dad. There was no reply. Peter's dad looked back and saw a very happy and a very tired boy fast asleep, clutching a piece of 'barfi', the sweet he enjoyed most.